HEALING IS A
CHOICE
Journal

HEALING IS A
CHOICE
Journal

⟶ STEPHEN ARTERBURN ⟵

NELSON BOOKS
A Division of Thomas Nelson Publishers
Since 1798

For other life-enriching books, visit us at:
www.thomasnelson.com

Published in Nashville, Tennessee, by Thomas Nelson, Inc.

Nelson Books titles may be purchased in bulk for educational, business,
fundraising, or sales promotional use. For information, please e-mail
SpecialMarkets@ThomasNelson.com.

ISBN: 0-7852-1873-4

Printed in the United States of America
1 2 3 4 5 6 QW 08 07 06 05

At one time or another, every human being needs healing. The type of healing needed will differ depending on who the person is and his or her circumstances. In every instance healing is a choice in which God and man are involved. Healing is a choice; it is God's choice. Also, there is a human side to the matter—there are choices we can make to ensure we experience whatever healing God, in His eternal purpose, has for us. Ultimately, however, we must remember the Creator of the universe is also the Healer of His universe. He is the ultimate decision maker as to how, when, and from whom we receive healing.

> *No matter how long you've struggled . . . it is time*
> *to pick up your mat and walk.*

_____

_____

_____

_____

_____

_____

_____

_____

_____

_____

_____

_____

_____

_____

_____

The First Choice:

The Choice to Connect Your Life

The First Big Lie:

"All I need to heal is just God and me."

You cannot read what God has to say about connecting with each other and be convinced that He wants us to face our pain with just Him and Him alone.

_____

_____

_____

_____

_____

_____

_____

_____

_____

_____

_____

_____

_____

- Romans 12:5 tells us to depend on each other, not to just depend on God.

- Romans 12:15 tells us to weep with each other, when we often want to just weep alone.

- Romans 15:14 tells us to counsel and teach each other, when we want to just wait and hear from God.

- I Corinthians 12:25 tells us to care for each other.

- I Thessalonians 5:11 tells us to encourage and build each other up.

- Ephesians 5:21 tells us to submit to each other, meaning you are to do more than just submit to God.

- Ephesians 4:2 tells us to uphold each other, when we try to act like we don't need anyone.

- Hebrews 10:24 tells us to stir up love in each other and share it.

- I Peter 4:10 tells us to minister to each other, so God's generosity is shared, not just enjoyed.

- James 5:16 tells us to tell each other what we have done wrong—then we can experience healing.

- Galatians 6:2 tells us to bear each other's burdens, when all we want to do is take them to God.

Over and over we see Scripture pushing us back toward each other. Connection is the way of God.

_____

_____

_____

_____

_____

_____

_____

_____

_____

_____

_____

_____

_____

> If you are living in isolation because
> of shame . . . know that God wants you out
> of hiding into the arms of a healing community.

_____

_____

_____

_____

_____

_____

_____

_____

_____

_____

_____

_____

_____

_____

_____

_____

You may find it in a church, some places of work, a small town, or a neighborhood. Community can be found, if you search for it.

_____

_____

_____

_____

_____

_____

_____

_____

_____

_____

_____

_____

_____

_____

_____

_____

_____

_____

_____

_____

_____

_____

_____

_____

_____

_____

_____

> *Connection with God is vital to our healing, but it is not enough. We must branch out from a "God only" mentality and reach out to others.*

THE SECOND CHOICE:

The Choice to Feel
Your Life

THE SECOND BIG LIE:

"Real Christians should have a real
peace in all circumstances."

> *You must feel before you can heal, or you will stay*
> *wounded and in turn wound others who get too close.*

_____

_____

_____

_____

_____

_____

_____

_____

_____

_____

_____

_____

_____

_____

_____

Almost everyone has experienced a loss or a trauma so bad that they were numb and unfeeling rather than overwhelmed by the intense pain. The shock and numbness is a unique gift from God that allows us to survive the worst emotions.

Do a pain inventory and a feelings checkup.
Find the time to get away, be still, and quiet your mind.
And ask yourself these questions:

What am I afraid of?

_____

_____

_____

_____

_____

What is missing?

_____

_____

_____

_____

_____

Why am I empty?

_____

_____

_____

_____

_____

_____

_____

What am I filling up on?

_____

_____

_____

_____

_____

_____

_____

What feelings am I avoiding?

_____

_____

_____

_____

_____

_____

_____

Why am I refusing to feel?

_____

_____

_____

_____

_____

_____

Why am I afraid of rejection?

_____

_____

_____

_____

_____

_____

_____

Why am I afraid of being inadequate?

_____

_____

_____

_____

_____

_____

Why am I afraid someone might come to control me?

_____

_____

_____

_____

_____

_____

In what ways do I avoid doing things for fear of failing?

_____

_____

_____

_____

_____

_____

I am afraid of doing nothing significant during my life . . .

_____

_____

_____

_____

_____

_____

_____

_____

_____

_____

_____

_____

_____

_____

_____

_____

When you have explored the fear, look at the anger:

When do I hold a grudge?

_____

_____

_____

_____

_____

_____

When am I angry because I feel controlled?

_____

_____

_____

_____

_____

_____

What areas of my past are in my present because of anger toward someone who hurt me?

_____

_____

_____

_____

_____

_____

In what ways am I seeking revenge in any form?

_____

_____

_____

_____

_____

_____

How does my anger lead me to negative statements about anyone?

_____

_____

_____

_____

_____

_____

_____

_____

_____

_____

_____

_____

_____

_____

_____

Then in the quiet moments, take a look at the guilt and shame you bear:

What feelings of guilt do I feel about a current habit?

_____

_____

_____

_____

_____

_____

What shame have I experienced from something someone did to me?

_____

_____

_____

_____

_____

Where am I knowingly involved in a sin?

_____

_____

_____

_____

_____

_____

When am I shutting down my guilt with food or drink?

_____

_____

_____

_____

_____

_____

_____

What could I change to reduce the guilt?

_____

_____

_____

_____

_____

_____

_____

_____

_____

_____

_____

_____

_____

_____

> *Jesus came so that we would no longer have to try to do what we cannot do.*
>
> ~~
>
> *"I am the way, the truth, and the life. No one comes to the Father except through Me"* (John 14:6 NKJV).

_____

_____

_____

_____

_____

_____

_____

_____

_____

_____

_____

_____

There is no reason to be anxious about anything when you have placed your trust in God (Phil. 4:6).

_____
_____
_____
_____
_____
_____
_____
_____
_____
_____
_____
_____
_____
_____

THE THIRD CHOICE:

*The Choice to Investigate
Your Life in Search of Truth*

THE THIRD BIG LIE:

*"It does no good to look
back or look inside."*

_____

_____

_____

_____

_____

_____

_____

_____

_____

_____

_____

_____

_____

_____

_____

_____

_____

_____

_____

"Let us . . . examine our ways" (Lam. 3:40 NKJV).

When you are willing to take a look, you may discover some areas that need work and that when worked on lead to healing.

Following are twenty questions that will aid in taking inventory of your life:

Starting as early as you can remember, who were the people in your life that hurt you?

_____

_____

_____

_____

Was there anything you did to bring on that hurt, or were they solely responsible?

_____

_____

_____

_____

_____

What was your reaction to that hurt? Did you forgive them, hold on to a grudge, or seek revenge?

_____

_____

_____

_____

_____

_____

In what ways, if any, could you have altered your reaction to the hurt?

_____

_____

_____

_____

_____

_____

Starting as early as you can remember, who were the people in your life that you hurt?

_____

_____

_____

_____

_____

_____

Did they do something first that hurt you, or were you acting without provocation?

_____

_____

_____

_____

_____

_____

Arrange your list of those you hurt in the order of the most damage to the least.

_____

_____

_____

_____

_____

_____

_____

_____

_____

_____

_____

_____

_____

_____

_____

_____

What was your reaction when you first realized you had hurt each person?

_____

_____

_____

_____

_____

What have you done to rectify the problem caused by your hurtful actions?

_____

_____

_____

_____

_____

_____

_____

How could you make restitution?

_____

_____

_____

_____

_____

_____

Are you aware of your five greatest strengths? Write down
what you think they are, and then ask five people to tell you
what they think they are.

_____

_____

_____

_____

_____

_____

Are you aware of your five greatest weaknesses? Write down what you think they are, and then ask the same five people to tell you what they think they are.

_____

_____

_____

_____

_____

What have you done to misuse your strengths? How have you been a good steward of them or wasted them?

_____

_____

_____

_____

_____

_____

_____

What have you done to use your strengths well? Ask those five people where they have seen you use them well.

_____

_____

_____

_____

_____

_____

What have you done to correct or work on your weaknesses?

_____

_____

_____

_____

_____

_____

What could you do to work on them further? Make a list.

_____

_____

_____

_____

_____

_____

_____

_____

_____

_____

_____

_____

_____

_____

_____

_____

_____

What could you do to make restitution to those you have hurt?

_____

_____

_____

_____

_____

_____

Who could help you walk through a path of forgiveness
toward those who have hurt you?

_____

_____

_____

_____

_____

_____

_____

Write down a plan to contact those you have hurt, and begin contacting them if it would not cause greater damage. What things did they tell you about yourself as you discussed the past?

_____

_____

_____

_____

_____

What person could be your partner in truth? How could that person help you discover the truth about yourself and motivate you to continue to work on the areas that need help?

_____

_____

_____

_____

_____

If you take these twenty steps, monitoring how you feel along the way and journaling those feelings and other insights, you will come to know yourself better. You will be taking what you know and using it to uncover what you do not know.

> "Those who are sad now are happy,
> because God will comfort them"
> (Matt. 5:4 NCV).

_____

_____

_____

_____

_____

_____

_____

_____

_____

_____

_____

_____

_____

_____

_____

THE FOURTH CHOICE:

The Choice to Heal Your Future

THE FOURTH BIG LIE:

"Time heals all wounds."

Anytime we drag our past into the future we have some grieving to do. When we refuse to grieve, we hang on to the weight of life that slows us down and robs us from finding our lives.

_____

_____

_____

_____

_____

_____

_____

_____

_____

_____

_____

_____

_____

_____

_____

_____

_____

_____

_____

_____

_____

_____

_____

_____

_____

_____

_____

_____

_____

"I tell you the truth, you will cry and be sad, but the world will be happy. You will be sad, but your sadness will become joy" (John 16:20 NCV).

> *Healing is a choice to let go of our past hurts by grieving them, and grieving is a choice to heal the future.*

_____

_____

_____

_____

_____

_____

_____

_____

_____

_____

_____

_____

_____

_____

THE FIFTH CHOICE:

The Choice to Help Your Life

THE FIFTH BIG LIE:

*"I can figure this out
by myself."*

"Right in front of every person is a path that is very wide and easy to follow" (Prov. 14:12, author's paraphrase).

> "Listen to advice and accept correction,
> and in the end you will be wise"
> (Prov. 19:20 NCV).

_____

_____

_____

_____

_____

_____

_____

_____

_____

_____

_____

_____

_____

_____

> *You are worth the effort, and God will honor your efforts to get the help you need to heal what is broken in your soul.*

_____

_____

_____

_____

_____

_____

_____

_____

_____

_____

_____

_____

_____

_____

_____

THE SIXTH CHOICE:

*The Choice to Embrace
Your Life*

THE SIXTH BIG LIE:

*"If I just act as if there is no problem,
it will finally go away."*

> *God will make the best come of the worst if you will trust in Him to do so.*

_____

_____

_____

_____

_____

_____

_____

_____

_____

_____

_____

_____

_____

_____

_____

_____

_____

_____

_____

_____

_____

_____

_____

_____

_____

_____

_____

For most people, embracing their own life comes down to making a radical adjustment of expectations. Alter your expectations and embrace the life you have, and you will live far beyond the expectations you had before.

"Be anxious for nothing, but in everything by prayer and supplication, with thanksgiving, let your requests be made known to God; and the peace of God, which surpasses all understanding, will guard your hearts and minds through Christ Jesus" (Phil. 4:6–7 NKJV).

_____

_____

_____

_____

_____

_____

_____

_____

_____

_____

_____

_____

_____

> "If anyone would come after me, he must deny himself and take up his cross daily and follow me. For whoever wants to save his life will lose it, but whoever loses his life for me will save it. What good is it for a man to gain the whole world, and yet lose or forfeit his very self?" (Luke 9:23–25 NIV).

_____

_____

_____

_____

_____

_____

_____

_____

_____

_____

_____

_____

THE SEVENTH CHOICE:

The Choice to Forgive

THE SEVENTH BIG LIE:

"Forgiveness is only for those who deserve it or earn it."

> The lack of forgiveness is a potent internal
> cocktail that you administer to yourself to your
> own detriment every day.

> "His compassions fail not. They are new every morning"
> (Lam. 3:22–23 NKJV).

_____

_____

_____

_____

_____

_____

_____

_____

_____

_____

_____

_____

_____

_____

_____

_____

_____

_____

_____

_____

_____

_____

_____

_____

_____

_____

_____

_____

_____

_____

*The hardness of another's heart is not an excuse for you
to harden yours. Forgive freely. Give forgiveness
from your heart so your heart can be free.*

A pretty sharp directive is found in Matthew 6:14–15: "If you forgive men when they sin against you, your heavenly Father will also forgive you. But if you do not forgive men their sins, your Father will not forgive your sins" (NIV)

_____

_____

_____

_____

_____

_____

_____

_____

_____

_____

_____

_____

_____

_____

_____

_____

_____

_____

_____

_____

_____

_____

_____

_____

_____

_____

Ephesians 4 tells us to get rid of all bitterness. So take a look at your life and see if there is anything there that is causing you to be bitter.

> "First be reconciled to your brother, and then come and offer your gift" (Matt. 5:24 NKJV).

_____

_____

_____

_____

_____

_____

_____

_____

_____

_____

_____

_____

_____

"Blessed be the God and Father of our Lord Jesus Christ, the Father of mercies and God of all comfort, who comforts us in all our tribulation that we may be able to comfort those who are in any trouble, with the comfort with which we ourselves are comforted by God" (2 Cor. 1:3–4 NKJV).

_____

_____

_____

_____

_____

_____

_____

_____

_____

_____

_____

_____

_____

_____

_____

_____

_____

_____

_____

_____

_____

_____

_____

_____

_____

_____

_____

"Lord, you are kind and forgiving and have great
love for those who call to you" (Ps. 86:5 NCV)

THE EIGHTH CHOICE:

The Choice to Risk Your Life

THE EIGHTH BIG LIE:

*"I must protect myself from
any more pain."*

> *The path of healing takes you through the depths of your feelings, grief, forgiveness, and the embracing of all of your life.*

_____

_____

_____

_____

_____

_____

_____

_____

_____

_____

_____

_____

_____

_____

_____

_____

_____

_____

_____

_____

_____

_____

_____

_____

_____

It might be a little embarrassing to ask someone to help
you get out of your comfort zone, but the world you are going
to live in is worth the risk—and so is the reward.

> "For God did not give us a spirit of timidity, but a spirit of power, of love and of self-discipline" (2 Tim. 1:7 NIV).

_____

_____

_____

_____

_____

_____

_____

_____

_____

_____

_____

_____

_____

_____

"Be strong and of good courage . . . for the LORD your God. He is the One who goes with you. He will not leave you nor forsake you" (Deut. 31:6 NKJV).

> You can't allow yourself to be healed if you are
> holding back and trying to protect yourself from
> what cannot be prevented—trials and sorrows.

_____

_____

_____

_____

_____

_____

_____

_____

_____

_____

_____

_____

_____

_____

_____

_____

_____

_____

_____

_____

_____

_____

_____

_____

_____

_____

_____

_____

_____

_____

_____

_____

_____

_____

_____

_____

_____

_____

_____

_____

_____

_____

> "Peace I leave with you; my peace I give you. I do not
> give to you as the world gives. Do not let your hearts be
> troubled and do not be afraid" (John 14:27 NIV).

THE NINTH CHOICE:

The Choice to Serve

THE NINTH BIG LIE:

*"Until I am completely healed
and strong there is no place
for me to serve God."*

> Serving is a choice to heal and come alive. It is the act of getting out of yourself and into others. It is the evidence that you "get it" when it comes to understanding how God works.

_____

_____

_____

_____

_____

_____

_____

_____

_____

_____

_____

_____

_____

THE TENTH CHOICE:

The Choice to Persevere

THE TENTH BIG LIE:

"There is no hope for me."

> *Healing is God's choice, and the timing of that choice and the method of the healing are His too.*

_____

_____

_____

_____

_____

_____

_____

_____

_____

_____

_____

_____

_____

_____

_____

_____

_____

_____

_____

_____

_____

_____

_____

_____

_____

_____

_____

_____

"The thief comes only to steal, and kill, and destroy;
I came that they might have life, and
might have it abundantly" (John 10:10 NASB).

> *Too often just before the evidence of God's work shows up,*
> *the person has already given up. Don't let that be you.*

_____

_____

_____

_____

_____

_____

_____

_____

_____

_____

_____

_____

_____

_____

As C. S. Lewis said, "Pain is at times God's megaphone to get through to us when other ways would do no good."

_____

_____

_____

_____

_____

_____

_____

_____

_____

_____

_____

_____

_____

_____

God lays a dark background and then just when it can be made no darker, there is a stroke of light. A brush stroke of gold or silver covers the darkness and brings glory to God.

Turn your life over to God. Surrender to His power.
Lie back into His arms and you will experience hope.

_____

_____

_____

_____

_____

_____

_____

_____

_____

_____

_____

_____

_____

_____

_____

_____

Healing is a Choice . . . challenge yourself to read "Today I Choose to Heal" every day for forty days. Throughout Scripture *forty days* pops up over and over again. Start your day, each day, for forty days by reading from the following pages the opening prayer and words of affirmation out loud in some quiet corner of your world.

If you accept this challenge it will:

+ implant in your heart and soul the words you need to persevere on the path to healing.
+ change the way you think about yourself.
+ change the way you think about life.

OPENING PRAYER

Lord, I am broken and hurting due to the brokenness of others and mistakes of my own. Please use your powers to heal me and give me courage to make the choices I need to make to allow Your healing in my life. Forgive me for standing in Your way of healing for me. Thank You for allowing my past to end one second ago, and my future to begin right now in this moment with you.

AFFIRMATION:

Today, I choose to heal.

My healing begins right now in this moment.

I am no longer bound by my sick past.

There is healing in my future.

For the next twenty-four hours I choose to live free and heal.

I choose to let go of past hurts that I cannot undo.

I choose to forgive myself for wrong choices in the past.

Today, I will dwell on what is good and right, not on the darkness I have experienced or the darkness others invite me to live.

Today I will live beyond myself and live for God.

On this day I will choose to feel my life rather than live in denial.

I will not medicate away my pain, sorrow, or anxiety.

I will allow each negative feeling to lead me to greater depths of healing.

I will not drown out or ignore my negative emotions.

I will work through these feelings and move out of them.

I will not project them on to those around me.

When I am unaware of what choice to make next, I will choose to do the next right thing.

Today I will not hide or run away.

I will connect with those who love me and with those who need my love.

Throughout this day I will stay connected to God and ask Him to guide me and lead me.

Today will be an adventure for me.

I will take a risk and enjoy the unpredictable.

I will not be governed by my fears.

I will choose to do something uncomfortable that might lead me to know the truth about myself or live life to the fullest.

I will not lie to myself today.

I will seek the truth and will ask for help when I need it.

Today I will reestablish some boundaries that will protect me from unhealthy people and unhealthy situations.

I will tear down some walls that are keeping some wonderful people from knowing me and loving me.

If there is some ungrieved loss, I will grieve it as much as I can today, and then put it away.

Today I will choose reality and embrace it.

I will accept my life and pick up my life right where it is.

I refuse to wallow in self-pity.

I will not focus on what I do not have or what might have been.

On this day I will not give up.

No matter how difficult the struggle, I choose to persevere.

I will not let any excuse be strong enough to derail my path to healing.

I will never give up or give in to an old life that did not serve me well.

I will allow no one to discourage me.

Today I will heal and rely on God to deliver it through the choices I make.

Today I will allow God to control my life, and each choice I make I will make with God in mind and love in my heart.

On this day, I choose healing.

I will do what I can do to heal and accept the limitations God has placed before me.

I will see every limitation I encounter as an invitation by God to do for me what I cannot do for myself.

I will accept that healing is sometimes slow and delayed, and I will grow in character in the mean time.

Today I will step outside myself and serve others.

I will find a need and fill it.

I will find the hurt of another and help heal it.

I will not become self-absorbed or filled with self-obsession.

I will reach out to someone in need and do what I can to meet that need.

Today I will ask for God's help to live out His purpose.

Today I will live for God and not myself.

Today, I choose to live.

Today, I choose to love.
Today, I choose to heal.

If you take my forty-day challenge, I would like to hear from you.

I would like to hear about your life before you took the challenge, while you were doing it, and afterward. Did it lead you to make healing choices? Let me know with an e-mail to Sarterburn@newlife.com. I may not know you personally, but this will give me a glimpse of your life. Please know that I am loving you and praying for God to bless you with new levels of healing for you and for your relationships.

—STEVE ARTERBURN

"Trust the LORD with all your heart, and don't depend on your own understanding. Remember the LORD in all you do, and He will give you success. Don't depend on your own wisdom. Respect the LORD and refuse to do wrong. Then your body will be healthy, and your bones will be strong" (Prov. 3:5–8 NCV)

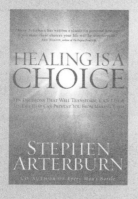
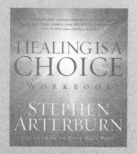

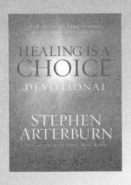

Healing Is a Choice Devotional: 10 Weeks of Transforming Brokenness into New Life

This 10-week devotional companion encourages and motivates readers to focus on the choices that enable true healing.

ISBN 1-4041-0210-8

Healing Is a Choice Small Group Kit

This curriculum explores 10 choices to make on the path toward healing. Each kit includes the book *Healing Is a Choice*, a workbook, a facilitator's guide, an instructional DVD, and a CD-Rom.

Available March 2006
ISBN 1-4185-0522-8

www.healingisachoice.org

"He heals the brokenhearted. And binds up their wounds."
—Psalm 147:3 NCV

NELSON BOOKS
A Division of Thomas Nelson Publishers
Since 1798

For other life-enriching books, visit us at:
www.thomasnelson.com